Brought to you from your friends at:

Written by: Phil Vischer and Melanie B. Rainer
Edited by: Melanie B. Rainer, Susan Manes and Denise George
Art Direction: Paul Conrad
Designed by:
John Trauscht — SpringSprang Studio
and Oed Ronne — Ronneland

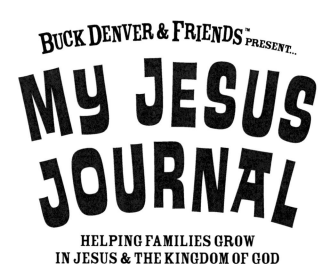

BUCK DENVER & FRIENDS™ PRESENT...

MY JESUS JOURNAL

HELPING FAMILIES GROW
IN JESUS & THE KINGDOM OF GOD

TABLE OF CONTENTS:

INTRODUCTION

The story of Jesus is so much more than the words we find written about his life on the pages of Matthew, Mark, Luke and John. It is the story that fundamentally changes everything, the greatest moment in all of human history, when God came to earth, died in our place, and set His people free forever. When we say, "He is risen!" at Easter, we are claiming something that is true every day. He is risen! The joy of the resurrection is part of the way we live every day of our lives. When Jesus came to earth, He brought the Kingdom of God to us, and planted it like a mustard seed. We are all invited to be part of the Kingdom - to stand fully redeemed, here and now. And yet we live and grow up in a still-broken world, but God has promised to make all things new.

My Jesus Journal is about more than learning about Christ, but learning to know Him.

My Jesus Journal was created to guide your family into a richer understanding of who we are, what Jesus did for us, and how we are to live in light of the truths of the Gospel. The Kingdom of God is here! It's blooming all around us, in big things and in everyday small things.

TIP! While *My Jesus Journal* wasn't specifically created for Easter, we've included tips throughout the book suggesting how you could use it during the Lent and Easter season. *My Jesus Journal* can be used anytime your family wants to spend time learning more about Christ and who He is. You could also use it if your children have questions about Jesus, or when they make the decision to follow Christ forever.

If you want to use *My Jesus Journal* during the Lent & Easter Season, we suggest the following framework:

- 2 Weeks Before Easter: Use the activities in the section "Who am I?"

- 1 Week Before Easter: Use the activities in the section "Who is Jesus?"

- Easter/Holy Week: Do the Remembering the Cross Family Activity

- Easter Week + Week After: Do activities in the section "How do we live because of Jesus?"

Online Extra:

Watch Phil Vischer talk more about celebrating Easter in the video "Phil Vischer on Easter" at **whatsinthebible.com/ myjesusjournal**. Or scan this QR code to watch from your phone. Your password is "**journal**."

What's Included:

- Instructions to make and use your Mustard Tree
- Family Activity List (use to fill in your Mustard Tree)
- Instructions for each child to make their own *My Jesus Journal*
- Activities for *My Jesus Journal*, broken down into 3 sections (Who Am I? Who is Jesus? How do we live because of Jesus?)
- Remembering the Cross Family Activity
- Additional Family Activities
- Online Access to videos and additional resources

Mustard Tree:

You can create a mustard tree to help remember your family's meaningful experiences. As you display your mustard tree in your home, the included leaves make it easy to remember and represent the things you are learning and ways you are participating in God's kingdom each day. Some of the included leaves provide ideas to help jumpstart your family time, and you also have a template to create leaves and write down your own ideas and experiences.

TIP! You can build your Mustard Tree during the Lent and Easter season, or during a month when your family is looking for something spiritual to do as a family to grow closer to God and to each other.

My Jesus Journal:

Each child can make a Jesus Journal to celebrate what makes him or her unique and to celebrate how much Jesus means to him or her. Anytime you see a page with a "MY JESUS JOURNAL" icon, it's your cue that this page can be part of your child's journal.

Have more than one child or need a do over? Additional copies can be printed from **whatsinthebible.com/myjesusjournal.**

Remembering the Cross:

Your family can walk through the events in Jesus' life leading up to His death and resurrection using the Remembering the Cross activity. This activity is divided up into seven events, making it easy to use throughout the week or all at once — whatever works best for your family.

 TIP! This activity is perfect for Holy Week, the week leading up to Easter. You could do an event each evening of Holy Week.

Additional Family Activities:

On those busy days you need something quick and easy-to-use, these activities are great. Each one has a corresponding leaf for your mustard tree.

 ## Online Access

To access videos, print off additional activity pages and more, visit **www.whatsinthebible.com/myjesusjournal.** Your password is: **journal**

Section 1:

YOUR MUSTARD TREE

Introduction

Make Your Own Mustard Tree Cut-Outs

Mustard Leaf Template

Family Activity Leaves

Introduction:

Jesus compares the Kingdom of God to a mustard seed – it will start small, and one day it will be in full bloom! God is continually renewing and restoring His Kingdom on earth. God calls us to join with Him in the renewal of His Kingdom, and there are many ways we can be good stewards of His Kingdom here and now. First, we are invited to join His Kingdom. God created everything, and He created each of us to be unique parts of the body of Christ. Throughout this journal, we will discover what it means to be a son or daughter of God, how Jesus brought the Kingdom of God to earth, and how we can live as citizens of God's Kingdom!

Add leaves to your tree anytime! You'll be amazed at how often leaves are added as your family becomes more aware of what everyone is learning about God and how He is active in every aspect of your lives. Your family will have a beautiful visual representation of the ways God is working in your lives and how you are participating in His Kingdom.

Online Extra:

Watch the video "Mustard Seed" at **whatsinthebible.com/myjesusjournal** or scan this QR code to watch on your phone.

What's Included:

- Mustard Tree Cut-Outs
- Mustard Leaf Template
- Fill-in-the-Blank Leaves
- Family Activity Leaves

Supplies You Will Need:

- White Poster Board
- Scissors
- Construction Paper or White Paper (for leaves)
- Crayons, Markers or Pens
- Glue or Tape

How To Build A Mustard Tree:

1. Build your Mustard Tree using the cut-outs provided. Cut out the trunk, branches, and verse, then glue the pieces to a poster board and display it in your home.

TIP! You can also draw your own tree on a poster board or piece of butcher paper, or purchase a plastic tree on which you can hang your leaves.

2. Using the Mustard Leaf Template found on page 37, cut out leaves from colored construction paper or plain white paper.
3. Cut out the provided Fill-in-the-Blank leaves, if you want to use them.
4. Cut out the Family Activity Leaves, if you want to use them.

TIP! Keep the blank leaves in a small basket or bowl near your Mustard Tree, so that it is easy to use them whenever you want!

Adding Leaves to Your Tree:

Your tree is a reflection of your family--what you love to do, what you are learning about God, and how He is working in your life! Here are some ideas for building your tree:

- Use the provided Family Activity Leaves to inspire fun things to do as a family at night or on the weekend. You'll find 3 categories of leaves — Acts of Service, Family Activities, and Love Your Neighbors. These are all ways you can see and be a part of the Kingdom of God in your life!
- Write prayer requests on leaves and post them to your tree
- Choose one color to represent each member of the family - and then every leaf they add to the tree can be that color or made out of that color paper
- Write one thing you are thankful for each day on a leaf
- Create your own ideas using the fill-in-the-blank and blank leaves.

MUSTARD TREE BRANCHES

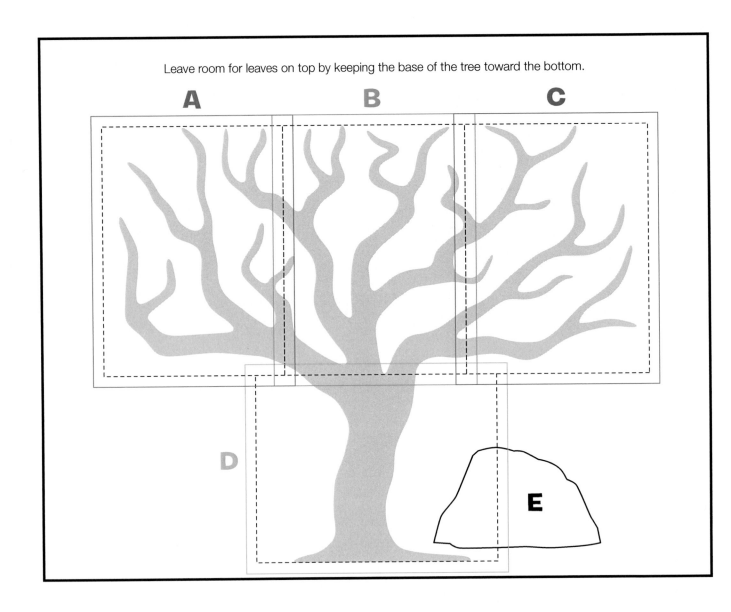

Leave room for leaves on top by keeping the base of the tree toward the bottom.

A   B   C

D

E

TIP! This page is INTENTIONALLY LEFT BLANK for those who choose to use the cut-outs from the book rather than printing. Remember, if you'd like to print the cut-outs, you can visit **www.whatsinthebible.com/myjesusjournal** and enter the password "**journal**" to access printable versions.

TIP! This page is INTENTIONALLY LEFT BLANK for those who choose to use the cut-outs from the book rather than printing. Remember, if you'd like to print the cut-outs, you can visit **www.whatsinthebible.com/myjesusjournal** and enter the password "**journal**" to access printable versions.

TIP! This page is INTENTIONALLY LEFT BLANK for those who choose to use the cut-outs from the book rather than printing. Remember, if you'd like to print the cut-outs, you can visit **www.whatsinthebible.com/myjesusjournal** and enter the password "**journal**" to access printable versions.

TIP! This page is INTENTIONALLY LEFT BLANK for those who choose to use the cut-outs from the book rather than printing. Remember, if you'd like to print the cut-outs, you can visit **www.whatsinthebible.com/myjesusjournal** and enter the password "**journal**" to access printable versions.

He told them another parable:
"The kingdom of heaven is like
a mustard seed, which a man took
and planted in his field. Though it is the
smallest of all seeds, yet when it grows, it is
the largest of garden plants and becomes a tree,
so that the birds come and perch in its branches."
– Matthew 13:31-32

E

TIP! This page is INTENTIONALLY LEFT BLANK for those who choose to use the cut-outs from the book rather than printing. Remember, if you'd like to print the cut-outs, you can visit **www.whatsinthebible.com/myjesusjournal** and enter the password "**journal**" to access printable versions.

MUSTARD TREE CONSTRUCTION

Here are some helpful pictures to show you how you could build your mustard tree:

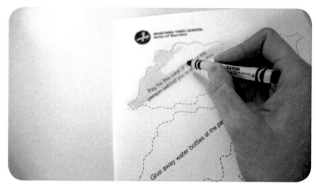

TIP! This page is INTENTIONALLY LEFT BLANK for those who choose to use the cut-outs from the book rather than printing. Remember, if you'd like to print the cut-outs, you can visit **www.whatsinthebible.com/myjesusjournal** and enter the password "**journal**" to access printable versions.

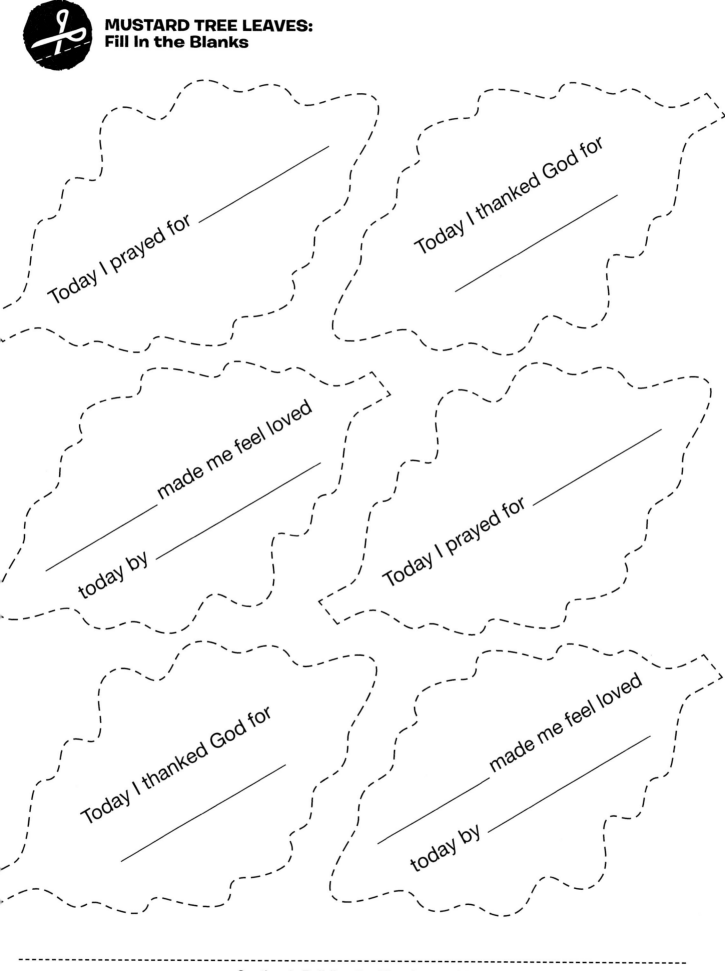

Today I prayed for _____

Today I thanked God for _____

_____ made me feel loved today by _____

Today I prayed for _____

Today I thanked God for _____

_____ made me feel loved today by _____

TIP! This page is INTENTIONALLY LEFT BLANK for those who choose to use the cut-outs from the book rather than printing. Remember, if you'd like to print the cut-outs, you can visit **www.whatsinthebible.com/myjesusjournal** and enter the password "**journal**" to access printable versions.

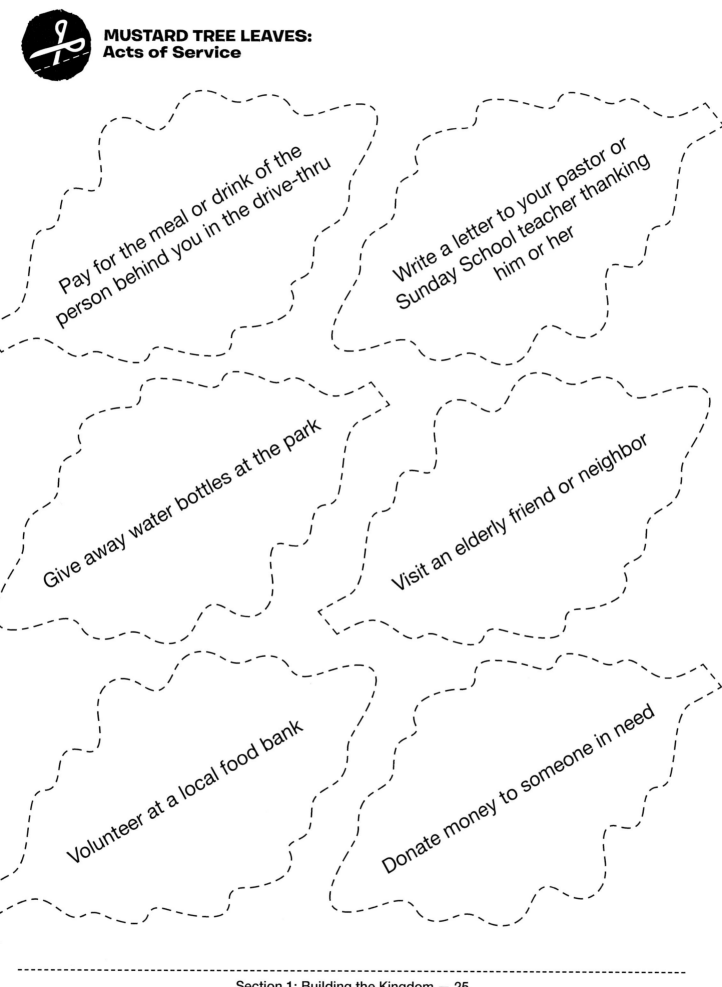

Pay for the meal or drink of the person behind you in the drive-thru

Write a letter to your pastor or Sunday School teacher thanking him or her

Give away water bottles at the park

Visit an elderly friend or neighbor

Volunteer at a local food bank

Donate money to someone in need

TIP! This page is INTENTIONALLY LEFT BLANK for those who choose to use the cut-outs from the book rather than printing. Remember, if you'd like to print the cut-outs, you can visit **www.whatsinthebible.com/myjesusjournal** and enter the password "**journal**" to access printable versions.

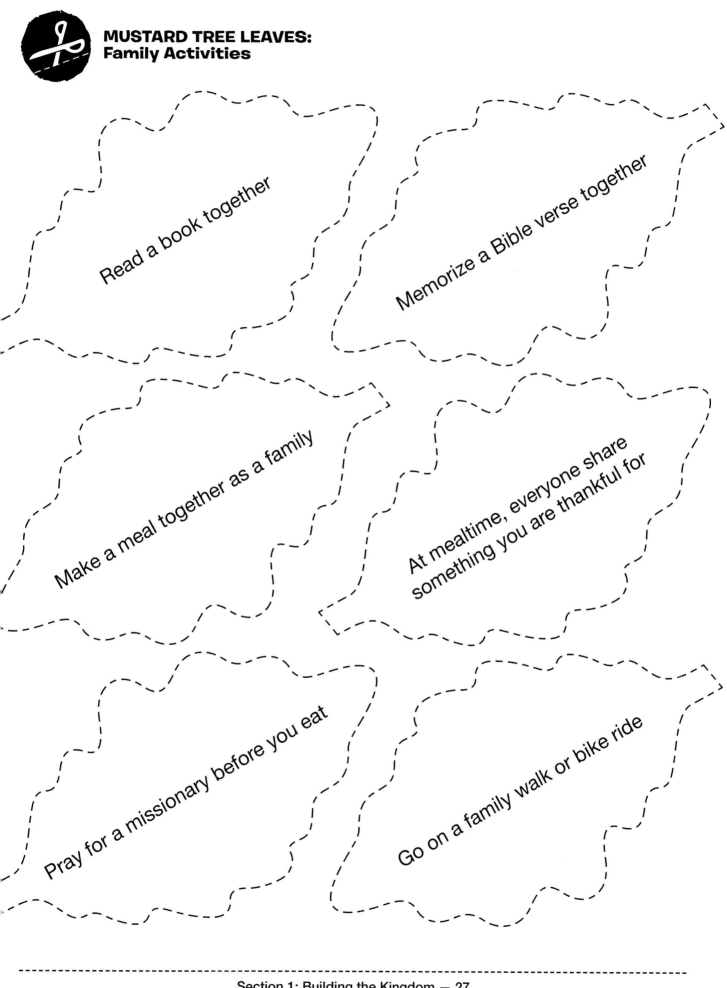

Read a book together

Memorize a Bible verse together

Make a meal together as a family

At mealtime, everyone share something you are thankful for

Pray for a missionary before you eat

Go on a family walk or bike ride

TIP! This page is INTENTIONALLY LEFT BLANK for those who choose to use the cut-outs from the book rather than printing. Remember, if you'd like to print the cut-outs, you can visit **www.whatsinthebible.com/myjesusjournal** and enter the password "**journal**" to access printable versions.

Create a family scavenger hunt

Take silly family pictures and make a collage or make a silly video

Watch a video together like *What's in the Bible?*

Play board games together as a family

Wardrobe Mixup! Each person picks out others' outfits and then have a fun family outing

Go on a drive to look at God's creation

TIP! This page is INTENTIONALLY LEFT BLANK for those who choose to use the cut-outs from the book rather than printing. Remember, if you'd like to print the cut-outs, you can visit **www.whatsinthebible.com/myjesusjournal** and enter the password "**journal**" to access printable versions.

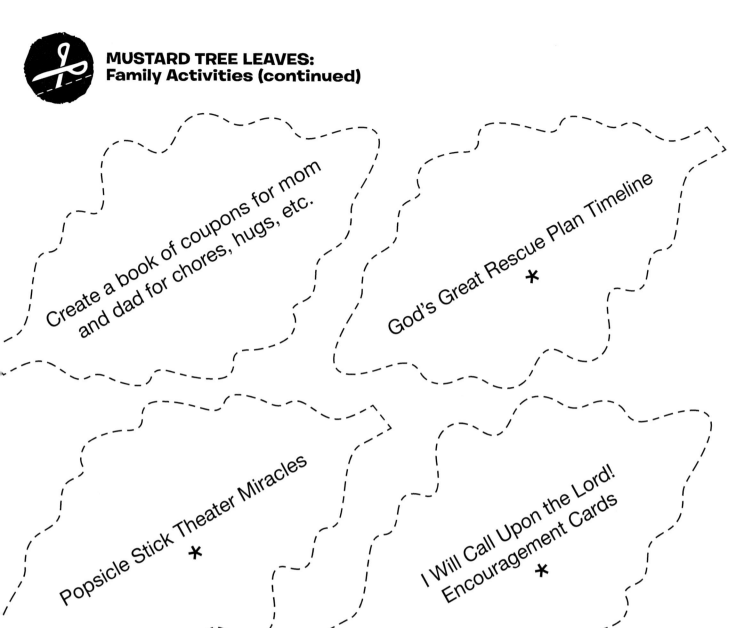

Create a book of coupons for mom and dad for chores, hugs, etc.

God's Great Rescue Plan Timeline
★

Popsicle Stick Theater Miracles
★

I Will Call Upon the Lord! Encouragement Cards
★

★ Find these activities in Section 7 (Page 105)

TIP! This page is INTENTIONALLY LEFT BLANK for those who choose to use the cut-outs from the book rather than printing. Remember, if you'd like to print the cut-outs, you can visit **www.whatsinthebible.com/myjesusjournal** and enter the password **"journal"** to access printable versions.

Bake cookies to take to your neighbors

Leave a thank you note and small gift in the mailbox for your mail carrier

Help your neighbor with yard work or snow removal

Have a play date with friends so their parents can run errands, etc

Go on a neighborhood prayer walk and pray for each house and family you walk by

Deliver a note to your neighbor's mailbox with an encouraging verse

TIP! This page is INTENTIONALLY LEFT BLANK for those who choose to use the cut-outs from the book rather than printing. Remember, if you'd like to print the cut-outs, you can visit **www.whatsinthebible.com/myjesusjournal** and enter the password "**journal**" to access printable versions.

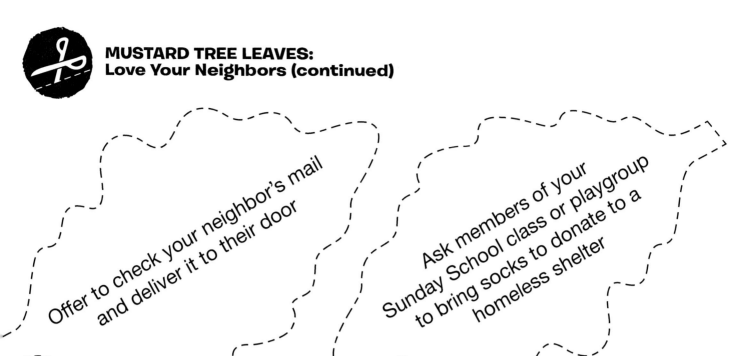

Offer to check your neighbor's mail and deliver it to their door

Ask members of your Sunday School class or playgroup to bring socks to donate to a homeless shelter

TIP! This page is INTENTIONALLY LEFT BLANK for those who choose to use the cut-outs from the book rather than printing. Remember, if you'd like to print the cut-outs, you can visit **www.whatsinthebible.com/myjesusjournal** and enter the password "**journal**" to access printable versions.

LEAF TEMPLATE

Use these leaves as a template to make your own! You can trace them onto construction paper or white paper and make as many as you need. Or visit **whatsinthebible.com/ myjesusjournal** to print multiple copies of this page.

TIP! This page is INTENTIONALLY LEFT BLANK for those who choose to use the cut-outs from the book rather than printing. Remember, if you'd like to print the cut-outs, you can visit **www.whatsinthebible.com/myjesusjournal** and enter the password **"journal"** to access printable versions.

Section 2:

MY JESUS JOURNAL

Introduction & Instructions

My Jesus Journal is an opportunity for each child to make their own journal – a record of the things they are learning about God and themselves. Children will have the chance to write poetry, letters, draw pictures, and create other pages for a journal that is unique to them! **The Mustard Tree** is a way for the whole family to engage in God's Kingdom together; **My Jesus Journal** is a way for each child to develop their own relationship with Jesus and see the way that He is working in their life.

The activities for My Jesus Journal are included in the next 4 sections. It works best to use these sections in order, because the finished journal will tell a story about each child and their relationship with Jesus.

How it works:

- Pages in this book for My Jesus Journal are marked with this special icon:

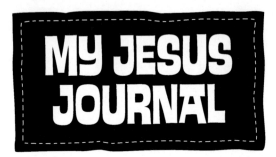

- Cut them out and have your child do the activity.
- Keep the pages together in a special place! You can keep them in a 3-ring binder, a folder, or punch holes in the pages and tie them together with yarn or string.

TIP! For additional copies of each page, or a downloadable PDF of the all the My Jesus Journal activities, visit whatsinthebible.com/myjesusjournal

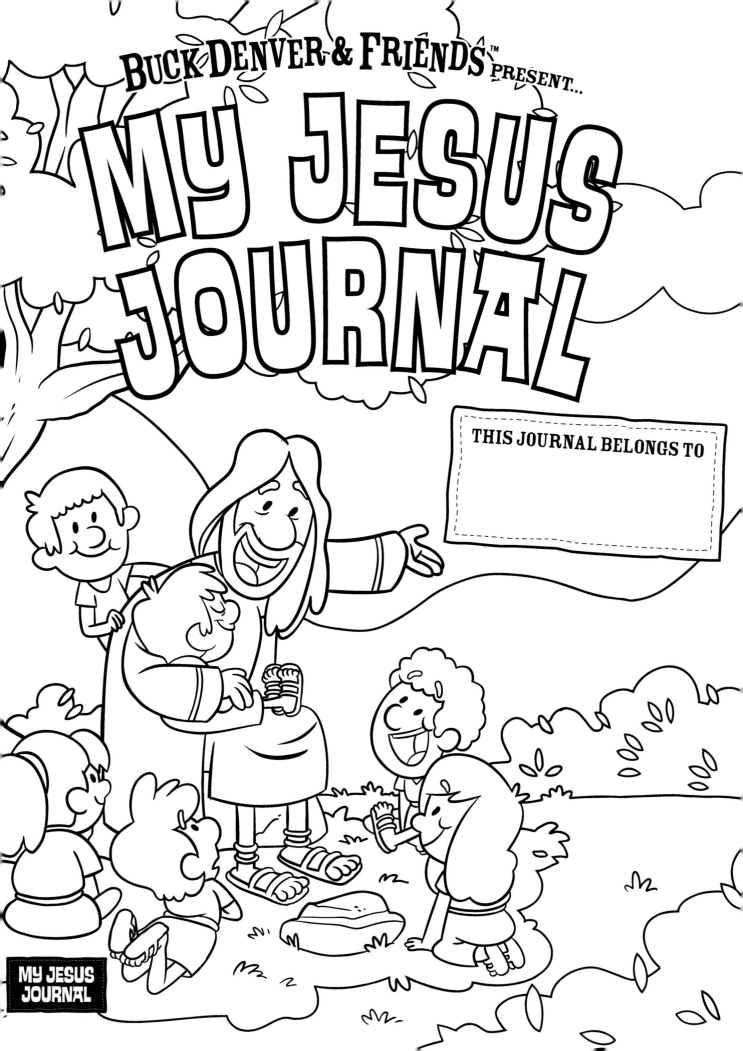

TIP! This page is INTENTIONALLY LEFT BLANK for those who choose to use the cut-outs from the book rather than printing. Remember, if you'd like to print the cut-outs, you can visit **www.whatsinthebible.com/myjesusjournal** and enter the password "**journal**" to access printable versions.

Section 3:

WHO AM I?

Who are we and why do we need Jesus? The
Old Testament is full of promises God made to His people.
Let's explore some of those promises, and learn about sin
and why God needed to send His son.

Psalm 139:14 Verse Coloring Page

I am Fearfully & Wonderfully Made Activity

My Favorite Things That God Has Created Activity

God Wants to Rescue Me Poem

Family Activity Suggestion:
God's Rescue Plan Timeline (Page 107-109)

TIP! This page is INTENTIONALLY LEFT BLANK for those who choose to use the cut-outs from the book rather than printing. Remember, if you'd like to print the cut-outs, you can visit **www.whatsinthebible.com/myjesusjournal** and enter the password "**journal**" to access printable versions.

I praise you, for I am fearfully and wonderfully made. Wonderful are your works; my soul knows it very well.

Psalm 139:14

©2013 Jellyfish One, LLC

TIP! This page is INTENTIONALLY LEFT BLANK for those who choose to use the cut-outs from the book rather than printing. Remember, if you'd like to print the cut-outs, you can visit **www.whatsinthebible.com/myjesusjournal** and enter the password "**journal**" to access printable versions.

I am fearfully and wonderfully made!

God made each one of us special and unique! He delights in you and made you to praise Him. Fill in the blanks with ways God made you YOU!

My name is _____.

My favorite thing to do is _____.

My favorite subject in school is _____.

My hair is _____ and my eyes are _____.

I love to praise God by _____.

I feel God's love when _____.

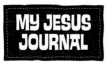

TIP! This page is INTENTIONALLY LEFT BLANK for those who choose to use the cut-outs from the book rather than printing. Remember, if you'd like to print the cut-outs, you can visit **www.whatsinthebible.com/myjesusjournal** and enter the password "**journal**" to access printable versions.

Draw a picture of yourself here!

 Write something unique about yourself on a leaf and put it on your mustard tree.

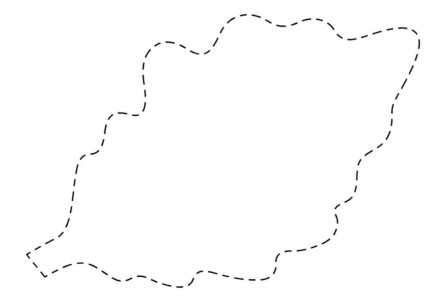

TIP! This page is INTENTIONALLY LEFT BLANK for those who choose to use the cut-outs from the book rather than printing. Remember, if you'd like to print the cut-outs, you can visit **www.whatsinthebible.com/myjesusjournal** and enter the password "**journal**" to access printable versions.

My favorite things that God has created!

We can be thankful to God for all of the good things He has created for us to enjoy. We serve such a creative God! Fill in the blanks with your favorite things.

My favorite place is _____

because _____.

My favorite animal is _____. **Draw a picture of it here:**

My favorite book is _____

because _____.

My favorite food is _____. **Draw a picture of it here:**

TIP! This page is INTENTIONALLY LEFT BLANK for those who choose to use the cut-outs from the book rather than printing. Remember, if you'd like to print the cut-outs, you can visit **www.whatsinthebible.com/myjesusjournal** and enter the password "**journal**" to access printable versions.

My favorite things that God has created! (continued)

My favorite color is _____.

My favorite season is _____. **Draw a picture of it here:**

Pray to God, thanking Him for each of these things!

Write something you are grateful for on a leaf and put it on your mustard tree.

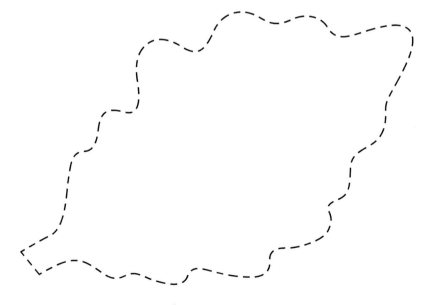

TIP! This page is INTENTIONALLY LEFT BLANK for those who choose to use the cut-outs from the book rather than printing. Remember, if you'd like to print the cut-outs, you can visit **www.whatsinthebible.com/myjesusjournal** and enter the password "**journal**" to access printable versions.

God wants me to be a part of His kingdom! Fill-in-the-poem

In this activity, you will fill in the last word of each line of the poem using the words at the bottom. Then on the next page, create your own poem, prayer or picture thanking God for sending His son!

Online Extra:

Watch Buck recite this poem at **whatsinthebible.com/ myjesusjournal**. Or scan this QR code to watch from your phone.

The first folks God made were Adam and Eve

They sinned in the Garden, so they had to _____

But God, in his love, launched a big plan

To save us from sin - like only he _____

For though we try hard to always be good

To follow God's laws, and act like we _____

To live life just right is a race we can't win

So Jesus came down to take ALL our _____ !

Once we know Jesus and make him our king

We're CLEAN in God's eyes - at last we can _____ !

Now nothing - no matter how high, deep or broad

Can take us away from the great love of _____ !

Words: *should, leave, God, sin, sing, can*

TIP! This page is INTENTIONALLY LEFT BLANK for those who choose to use the cut-outs from the book rather than printing. Remember, if you'd like to print the cut-outs, you can visit **www.whatsinthebible.com/myjesusjournal** and enter the password "**journal**" to access printable versions.

Create your own!

In this space, create your own poem, prayer or picture thanking God for rescuing us.

TIP! This page is INTENTIONALLY LEFT BLANK for those who choose to use the cut-outs from the book rather than printing. Remember, if you'd like to print the cut-outs, you can visit **www.whatsinthebible.com/myjesusjournal** and enter the password "**journal**" to access printable versions.

Section 4:

WHO IS JESUS?

In this section, we will learn about the life & ministry of
Jesus and how he established the kingdom of God on earth.

John 3:16 Verse Coloring Page

Jesus Timeline

Names of Jesus

Family Activity Suggestion:
Popsicle Stick Theater Miracles (Page 111-115)

TIP! This page is INTENTIONALLY LEFT BLANK for those who choose to use the cut-outs from the book rather than printing. Remember, if you'd like to print the cut-outs, you can visit **www.whatsinthebible.com/myjesusjournal** and enter the password "**journal**" to access printable versions.

For God so LOVED the world, that he gave his only Son, that whoever believes in him should NOT perish but have ETERNAL LIFE.

John 3:16

TIP! This page is INTENTIONALLY LEFT BLANK for those who choose to use the cut-outs from the book rather than printing. Remember, if you'd like to print the cut-outs, you can visit **www.whatsinthebible.com/myjesusjournal** and enter the password "**journal**" to access printable versions.

Jesus Timeline

Use this timeline to draw the big events of Jesus' life! What do you think things would have looked like when Jesus was a boy?

Jesus is born in a stable in Bethlehem. Luke 2:1-7

Jesus and his family live in Egypt to hide from Herod. Matthew 2:13-15

Jesus preaches at the temple when he is a young boy. Luke 2:41-51

TIP! This page is INTENTIONALLY LEFT BLANK for those who choose to use the cut-outs from the book rather than printing. Remember, if you'd like to print the cut-outs, you can visit **www.whatsinthebible.com/myjesusjournal** and enter the password "**journal**" to access printable versions.

Jesus Timeline (continued)

Jesus is a carpenter. Mark 6:3

Jesus is baptized in the river by John the Baptist. Luke 3:21-22

Jesus calls his 12 disciples. Mark 3:13-14

TIP! This page is INTENTIONALLY LEFT BLANK for those who choose to use the cut-outs from the book rather than printing. Remember, if you'd like to print the cut-outs, you can visit **www.whatsinthebible.com/myjesusjournal** and enter the password "**journal**" to access printable versions.

Names of Jesus

The Bible uses many different names and images for Jesus. Some are in the Old Testament and some are in the New Testament. Go through the following verse cards and color in the name for Jesus on each. Then on the next page, write your favorite name or symbol for Jesus and draw a picture representing it or write why you like that name so much.

"I am the Alpha and the Omega," says the Lord God, "who is and who was and who is to come, the Almighty."

Revelation 1:8

"As I looked, thrones were placed, and the Ancient of Days took his seat; his clothing was white as snow, and the hair of his head like pure wool … "

Daniel 7:9

Jesus said to them, "I am the bread of life; whoever comes to me shall not hunger, and whoever believes in me shall never thirst."

John 6:35

"I, Jesus, have sent my angel to testify to you about these things for the churches. I am the root and the descendant of David, the bright morning star."

Revelation 22:16

TIP! This page is INTENTIONALLY LEFT BLANK for those who choose to use the cut-outs from the book rather than printing. Remember, if you'd like to print the cut-outs, you can visit **www.whatsinthebible.com/myjesusjournal** and enter the password "**journal**" to access printable versions.

"and he looked at Jesus as he walked by and said, "Behold, the Lamb of God!"

John 1:36

The Lord is my shepherd; I shall not want.

Psalm 23:1

I am the true vine, and my Father is the vinedresser.

John 15:1

TIP! This page is INTENTIONALLY LEFT BLANK for those who choose to use the cut-outs from the book rather than printing. Remember, if you'd like to print the cut-outs, you can visit **www.whatsinthebible.com/myjesusjournal** and enter the password "**journal**" to access printable versions.

My Favorite Name for Jesus is:

TIP! This page is INTENTIONALLY LEFT BLANK for those who choose to use the cut-outs from the book rather than printing. Remember, if you'd like to print the cut-outs, you can visit **www.whatsinthebible.com/myjesusjournal** and enter the password "**journal**" to access printable versions.

Section 5:

REMEMBERING THE CROSS FAMILY ACTIVITY

Perfect for the whole family, this activity is to help you understand and reflect upon the events of Holy Week, Christ's Death, and His Resurrection.

Each Remember Page includes 3 components: Read, Reflect, Create.

As the whole family goes through each event, each child can fill out the corresponding remember page in their Jesus Journal. Encourage your child to write down or draw any thoughts or feelings they experienced during that time on their journal page.

You may cut out the pages from this book, or you can print extra copies from **whatsinthebible.com/myjesusjournal**

Remember Pages

Coloring & Reflection Pages for My Jesus Journal

Online Extra:

Watch the video *Remembering the Cross* at **whatsinthebible.com/myjesusjournal**. Or scan this QR code to watch from your phone.

TIP! This is a great activity to do during Holy Week, the week leading up to Easter. You can do one page each night of Holy Week, or you can do them all together one evening.

Remember: Passover

Read: Exodus 12: 21-24

Reflect: The Lord protected the firstborn sons of the Israelites from death on the night of the Passover. We can remember Passover because it reminds us of the sacrifice Jesus, a perfect lamb, made when He saved us from death forever. If you had been there for the first Passover, would you have been scared? Are there things that you are afraid of now? Let's pray to God, asking Him to help us to not be afraid.

Create: Coloring Page (p. 77)

Remember: Palm Sunday

Read: John 12:12-15

Reflect: The people of Jerusalem knew that Jesus was their Messiah! They honored Him on that day when they waved their palm branches and cried "Hosanna!" Can you imagine what it would have been like to be there and see Jesus?

Create: Coloring Page (p. 79)

Remember: The Last Supper

Read: Luke 22: 14-23

Reflect: Does this sound familiar? We practice communion at church as a way of remembering Jesus the same way His disciples did at the Passover meal on the night before Jesus died. Jesus tells His disciples that His body will be broken and His blood will be shed for them. He calls it a "new covenant."

Create: Coloring Page (p. 81)

Remember: Jesus Prays in the Garden

Read: Luke 22:39-44

Reflect: Jesus knew what was about to happen to Him, but He trusted God and His perfect plan. Jesus was about to die so that we could be with God forever! Jesus prayed and trusted God in the most difficult of circumstances. When we face difficult things in our lives, we can also pray to God for strength and know that He knows how we feel.

Create: Coloring Page (p. 83)

Remember: Jesus is Betrayed

Read: Mark 14:43-50

Reflect: When Judas betrayed Jesus and He was captured, Jesus said "let the Scriptures be fulfilled." Jesus knew that He was the Messiah that everyone had been waiting for since sin had entered the world!

Create: Coloring Page (p. 85)

Remember: Jesus is Killed

Read: Mark 15:33-39

Reflect: When Jesus died, the whole earth was dark. The curtain in the Jewish temple was ripped in two! The people realized that Jesus truly was the Son of God, the King they had been waiting for. It was a very sad day in all of creation. On Good Friday each year, we also remember what a sad day it was – and it is ok to be sad, even though we know that Jesus rose again! Jesus died to save a broken world, and we still live in a broken world, but know that He will come again.

Create: Coloring Page (p. 87)

Remember: He Lives!

Read: Mark 16:1-7

Reflect: Jesus is alive! He conquered death so that we can live with Him in the Kingdom of God forever! When Jesus defeated death, He defeated death for all of us. We don't have to live in fear, and God promises that we will live with Him forever. Because Jesus paid the price for our sins, when God looks at us He sees how Jesus made us clean. Can you think of any favorite worship songs or hymns that we can sing together in celebration? Let's sing a song or pray together giving thanks for Jesus's death and resurrection!

Create: Coloring Page (p. 89)

TIP! This page is INTENTIONALLY LEFT BLANK for those who choose to use the cut-outs from the book rather than printing. Remember, if you'd like to print the cut-outs, you can visit **www.whatsinthebible.com/myjesusjournal** and enter the password "**journal**" to access printable versions.

TIP! This page is INTENTIONALLY LEFT BLANK for those who choose to use the cut-outs from the book rather than printing. Remember, if you'd like to print the cut-outs, you can visit **www.whatsinthebible.com/myjesusjournal** and enter the password "**journal**" to access printable versions.

TIP! This page is INTENTIONALLY LEFT BLANK for those who choose to use the cut-outs from the book rather than printing. Remember, if you'd like to print the cut-outs, you can visit **www.whatsinthebible.com/myjesusjournal** and enter the password "**journal**" to access printable versions.

TIP! This page is INTENTIONALLY LEFT BLANK for those who choose to use the cut-outs from the book rather than printing. Remember, if you'd like to print the cut-outs, you can visit **www.whatsinthebible.com/myjesusjournal** and enter the password "**journal**" to access printable versions.

TIP! This page is INTENTIONALLY LEFT BLANK for those who choose to use the cut-outs from the book rather than printing. Remember, if you'd like to print the cut-outs, you can visit **www.whatsinthebible.com/myjesusjournal** and enter the password "**journal**" to access printable versions.

TIP! This page is INTENTIONALLY LEFT BLANK for those who choose to use the cut-outs from the book rather than printing. Remember, if you'd like to print the cut-outs, you can visit **www.whatsinthebible.com/myjesusjournal** and enter the password "**journal**" to access printable versions.

TIP! This page is INTENTIONALLY LEFT BLANK for those who choose to use the cut-outs from the book rather than printing. Remember, if you'd like to print the cut-outs, you can visit **www.whatsinthebible.com/myjesusjournal** and enter the password "**journal**" to access printable versions.

HOW DO WE LIVE BECAUSE OF JESUS?

In this section, explore what it means that Jesus died for us.
How do we live because Jesus has made us new?

2 Corinthians 5:17 Coloring Page

Who Am I? (A New Creation Version)

I Want to Be in the Kingdom of God Map

What Jesus Means to Me

Suggested Family Activity:
I Will Call Upon the Lord! Encouragement Cards (Page 117-119)

TIP! This page is INTENTIONALLY LEFT BLANK for those who choose to use the cut-outs from the book rather than printing. Remember, if you'd like to print the cut-outs, you can visit **www.whatsinthebible.com/myjesusjournal** and enter the password "**journal**" to access printable versions.

Therefore, if anyone is in Christ, he is a new creation. The old has passed away; behold, the new has come.

2 Corinthians 5:17

TIP! This page is INTENTIONALLY LEFT BLANK for those who choose to use the cut-outs from the book rather than printing. Remember, if you'd like to print the cut-outs, you can visit **www.whatsinthebible.com/myjesusjournal** and enter the password "**journal**" to access printable versions.

Who am I? (A new creation version)

When we become a part of God's Kingdom, we are a new creation. We are free from the sin that kept us away from God. When God looks at us, He sees us the way He sees Jesus.

 Read Colossians 3:12-17. These verses tell us to "put on" things that show we are a new creation in Christ. Decorate the person below to be you. Add your hair and eyes and smile, and then color the cut-outs on the next page and glue them on to your drawing.

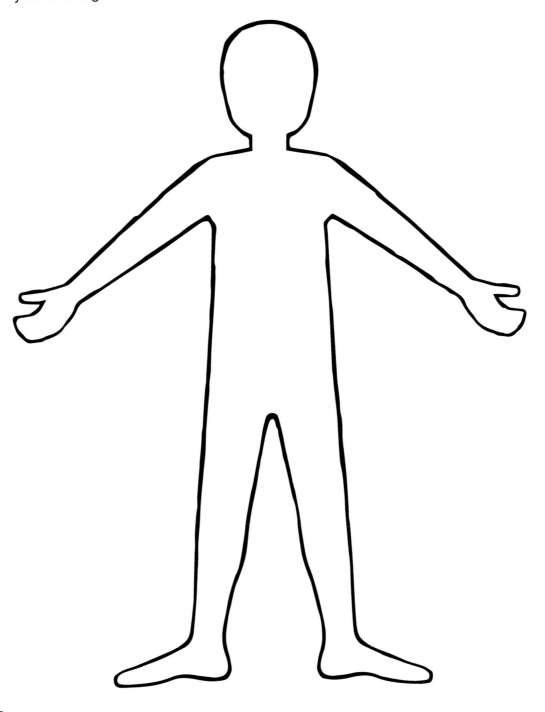

TIP! This page is INTENTIONALLY LEFT BLANK for those who choose to use the cut-outs from the book rather than printing. Remember, if you'd like to print the cut-outs, you can visit **www.whatsinthebible.com/myjesusjournal** and enter the password "**journal**" to access printable versions.

TIP! This page is INTENTIONALLY LEFT BLANK for those who choose to use the cut-outs from the book rather than printing. Remember, if you'd like to print the cut-outs, you can visit **www.whatsinthebible.com/myjesusjournal** and enter the password "**journal**" to access printable versions.

I Want to Be in the Kingdom of God Map

Ian sings a song in *What's in the Bible? Volume 10* about what it means to be in the Kingdom of God and share it with everyone we meet. Use the map on the next page to think about how you can share the Kingdom of God in each place. Use the space below each place to write ideas or draw pictures about how you can impact each one. Some ideas include: praying for the people there, donating money or things, serving, meeting new people, etc.

Online Extra:

Watch "I Want to Be in the Kingdom of God" at **whatsinthebible.com/myjesusjournal**. Or scan this QR code to watch from your phone.

I'd like to be in the kingdom of God,

Where there's no cryin'

There's no dyin'

It makes me want to applaud and say "Hey God, you're fantastic!"

And I am so enthusiastic

We'll redeem creation,

and I get to share your invitation

with everybody, with everybody I meet.

TIP! This page is INTENTIONALLY LEFT BLANK for those who choose to use the cut-outs from the book rather than printing. Remember, if you'd like to print the cut-outs, you can visit **www.whatsinthebible.com/myjesusjournal** and enter the password "**journal**" to access printable versions.

I Want to Be in the Kingdom of God Map

MY HEART

MY HOUSE

MY CHURCH

MY NEIGHBORHOOD

MY CITY

MY WORLD

TIP! This page is INTENTIONALLY LEFT BLANK for those who choose to use the cut-outs from the book rather than printing. Remember, if you'd like to print the cut-outs, you can visit **www.whatsinthebible.com/myjesusjournal** and enter the password "**journal**" to access printable versions.

What Jesus means to me!

Use the space below to share what the Jesus means to you. You can draw a picture, write a poem, write a letter to Jesus, make an acrostic, or create a collage. Have fun! Each person can make something they enjoy. As you gather together as a family during a meal or before bed, talk about each person's creation and what Jesus means to him or her.

TIP! This page is INTENTIONALLY LEFT BLANK for those who choose to use the cut-outs from the book rather than printing. Remember, if you'd like to print the cut-outs, you can visit **www.whatsinthebible.com/myjesusjournal** and enter the password "**journal**" to access printable versions.

Section 7:

FAMILY ACTIVITIES

The fun family activities each correspond with a
Family Activity leaf from Section 1.

God's Great Rescue Plan Timeline

Popsicle Stick Theater Miracles

I Will Call Upon the Lord! Encouragement Cards

TIP! This page is INTENTIONALLY LEFT BLANK for those who choose to use the cut-outs from the book rather than printing. Remember, if you'd like to print the cut-outs, you can visit **www.whatsinthebible.com/myjesusjournal** and enter the password "**journal**" to access printable versions.

God's Rescue Plan Timeline

INSTRUCTIONS After sin entered the world, God launched a rescue plan! Trace His timeline from Adam and Eve to Jesus. Cut out and color each image from the next page, then match it with the description on the timeline. Read the Bible verses listed if you need a hint, or want to learn more.

Find, cut & paste picture here from next page.

When they chose to eat the fruit from the tree God told them not to eat from, sin entered the world. We became separated from God.

Read: GENESIS 3

God called him to leave Ur and promised that he would become the father of many, and through him everyone on earth would be blessed.

Read: GENESIS 17:3-6

Find, cut & paste picture here from next page.

Find, cut & paste picture here from next page.

He led God's people out of slavery in Egypt and toward the Promised Land.

Read: EXODUS 3:10-12

He finished leading the Israelites into the Promised Land with help from God in big battles, like Jericho!

Find, cut & paste picture here from next page.

Find, cut & paste picture here from next page.

He became king after Saul. God promised him that someone from his family would rule over God's people forever.

Read: 2 SAMUEL 7:4-17

Read: JOSHUA 6:1-2

But God's people kept turning away from Him! So He did what He promised – and Israel and Judah were conquered.

Read: 2 KINGS 18:11-12

Find, cut & paste picture here from next page.

Find, cut & paste picture here from next page.

God sent this prophet to tell the Israelites that a Messiah was coming to save them and be their king.

Read: ISAIAH 9:1-7

After 400 years, the Messiah was born. He is the king from the line of David who will establish God's kingdom on earth!

Find, cut & paste picture here from next page.

Read: LUKE 2:1-6

ONLINE EXTRA!

Watch God's Rescue Plan Recap at **whatsinthebible.com/myjesusjournal** or scan the QR code to watch on your phone.

TIP! This page is INTENTIONALLY LEFT BLANK for those who choose to use the cut-outs from the book rather than printing. Remember, if you'd like to print the cut-outs, you can visit **www.whatsinthebible.com/myjesusjournal** and enter the password "**journal**" to access printable versions.

Color and cut these pictures and paste them onto the timeline of the previous page!

TIP! This page is INTENTIONALLY LEFT BLANK for those who choose to use the cut-outs from the book rather than printing. Remember, if you'd like to print the cut-outs, you can visit **www.whatsinthebible.com/myjesusjournal** and enter the password "**journal**" to access printable versions.

POPSICLE STICK THEATER MIRACLES

Use these popsicle stick cut-outs to perform your own puppet shows of Jesus' miracles. Read the verses or watch the video to remember the stories!

Read: MATTHEW 8:23-27

Watch: Visit **whatsinthebible.com/myjesusjournal** to watch a video of this miracle! Or scan the QR code to watch it on your phone!

JESUS CALMS THE STORM!

TIP! This page is INTENTIONALLY LEFT BLANK for those who choose to use the cut-outs from the book rather than printing. Remember, if you'd like to print the cut-outs, you can visit **www.whatsinthebible.com/myjesusjournal** and enter the password "**journal**" to access printable versions.

Read:
MATTHEW 9: 1-8

Watch: Visit **whatsinthebible.com/myjesusjournal** to watch a video of this miracle! Or scan the QR code to watch it on your phone!

JESUS HEALS THE PARALYZED MAN!

TIP! This page is INTENTIONALLY LEFT BLANK for those who choose to use the cut-outs from the book rather than printing. Remember, if you'd like to print the cut-outs, you can visit **www.whatsinthebible.com/myjesusjournal** and enter the password "**journal**" to access printable versions.

POPSICLE STICK THEATER MIRACLES

Read: MATTHEW 14:13-21

Watch: Visit **whatsinthebible.com/myjesusjournal** to watch a video of this miracle! Or scan the QR code to watch it on your phone!

JESUS FEEDS THE 5000!

TIP! This page is INTENTIONALLY LEFT BLANK for those who choose to use the cut-outs from the book rather than printing. Remember, if you'd like to print the cut-outs, you can visit **www.whatsinthebible.com/myjesusjournal** and enter the password "**journal**" to access printable versions.

CALL UPON THE LORD!
ENCOURAGEMENT CARDS

The Bible is full of encouraging words for us! When we are tired, sad, scared or facing something that is hard, we can call upon the Lord for strength. Below are some encouraging verses that remind us of God's promises. You can decorate these great reminders and place them around your house (on the fridge, the mirror, next to your bed) or share them with others who need encouragement.

"Fear not, for I am with you; be not dismayed, for I am your God; I will strengthen you, I will help you, I will uphold you with my righteous right hand."

ISAIAH 41:10

"The Lord your God is in your midst, a mighty one who will save; he will rejoice over you with gladness, he will quiet you by his love; he will exult over you with loud singing."

ZEPHANIAH 3:17

"Peace I leave with you; my peace I give to you. Not as the world gives do I give to you. Let not your hearts be troubled, neither let them be afraid."

JOHN 14:27

TIP! This page is INTENTIONALLY LEFT BLANK for those who choose to use the cut-outs from the book rather than printing. Remember, if you'd like to print the cut-outs, you can visit **www.whatsinthebible.com/myjesusjournal** and enter the password "**journal**" to access printable versions.

CALL UPON THE LORD!
ENCOURAGEMENT CARDS

"Do not be anxious about anything, but in everything by prayer and supplication with thanksgiving let your requests be made known to God."

PHILIPPIANS 4:6

"For I am sure that neither death nor life, nor angels nor rulers, nor things present nor things to come, nor powers, nor height nor depth, nor anything else in all creation, will be able to separate us from the love of God in Christ Jesus our Lord."

ROMANS 8:38-39

"The Lord is my light and my salvation; whom shall I fear? The Lord is the stronghold of my life; of whom shall I be afraid?"

PSALM 27:1

TIP! This page is INTENTIONALLY LEFT BLANK for those who choose to use the cut-outs from the book rather than printing. Remember, if you'd like to print the cut-outs, you can visit **www.whatsinthebible.com/myjesusjournal** and enter the password "**journal**" to access printable versions.

$5 OFF

EXCLUSIVE OFFER FOR
Friends & Family

THE BIBLE MADE EASY.
BEGIN THE JOURNEY TODAY.

COUPON CODE:
FRIEND5P

REDEEM NOW AT
WHATSINTHEBIBLE.COM

$5 OFF

EXCLUSIVE OFFER FOR
Friends & Family

THE BIBLE MADE EASY.
BEGIN THE JOURNEY TODAY.

COUPON CODE:
FRIEND5P

REDEEM NOW AT
WHATSINTHEBIBLE.COM

$5 OFF

EXCLUSIVE OFFER FOR
Friends & Family

THE BIBLE MADE EASY.
BEGIN THE JOURNEY TODAY.

COUPON CODE:
FRIEND5P

REDEEM NOW AT
WHATSINTHEBIBLE.COM

$5 OFF

EXCLUSIVE OFFER FOR
Friends & Family

THE BIBLE MADE EASY.
BEGIN THE JOURNEY TODAY.

COUPON CODE:
FRIEND5P

REDEEM NOW AT
WHATSINTHEBIBLE.COM

$5 OFF

EXCLUSIVE OFFER FOR
Friends & Family

THE BIBLE MADE EASY.
BEGIN THE JOURNEY TODAY.

COUPON CODE:
FRIEND5P

REDEEM NOW AT
WHATSINTHEBIBLE.COM

$5 OFF

EXCLUSIVE OFFER FOR
Friends & Family

THE BIBLE MADE EASY.
BEGIN THE JOURNEY TODAY.

COUPON CODE:
FRIEND5P

REDEEM NOW AT
WHATSINTHEBIBLE.COM

$5 OFF

EXCLUSIVE OFFER FOR
Friends & Family

THE BIBLE MADE EASY.
BEGIN THE JOURNEY TODAY.

COUPON CODE:
FRIEND5P

REDEEM NOW AT
WHATSINTHEBIBLE.COM

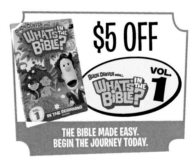

$5 OFF

EXCLUSIVE OFFER FOR
Friends & Family

THE BIBLE MADE EASY.
BEGIN THE JOURNEY TODAY.

COUPON CODE:
FRIEND5P

REDEEM NOW AT
WHATSINTHEBIBLE.COM

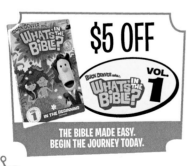

$5 OFF

EXCLUSIVE OFFER FOR
Friends & Family

THE BIBLE MADE EASY.
BEGIN THE JOURNEY TODAY.

COUPON CODE:
FRIEND5P

REDEEM NOW AT
WHATSINTHEBIBLE.COM

$5 OFF

EXCLUSIVE OFFER FOR
Friends & Family

THE BIBLE MADE EASY.
BEGIN THE JOURNEY TODAY.

COUPON CODE:
FRIEND5P

REDEEM NOW AT
WHATSINTHEBIBLE.COM

TIP! This page is INTENTIONALLY LEFT BLANK for those who choose to use the cut-outs from the book rather than printing. Remember, if you'd like to print the cut-outs, you can visit **www.whatsinthebible.com/myjesusjournal** and enter the password "**journal**" to access printable versions.

Made in the USA
Middletown, DE
08 March 2015